P9-BXX-346

Ganesha

The God of Prosperity

An imprint of Om Books International

Reprinted in 2017 by

An imprint of Om Books International

Corporate & Editorial Office
A 12, Sector 64, Noida 201 301
Uttar Pradesh, India
Phone: +91 120 477 4100
Email: editorial@ombooks.com
Website: www.ombooksinternational.com

Sales Office
107, Ansari Road, Darya Ganj,
New Delhi 110 002, India
Phone: +91 11 4000 9000, 2326 3363, 2326 5303
Fax: +91 11 2327 8091
Email: sales@ombooks.com
Website: www.ombooks.com

Copyright © Om Books International 2008

ALL RIGHTS RESERVED. No part of this book may be reproduced or transmitted in any form by any means, electronic or mechanical, including photocopying and recording, or by any information storage and retrieval system, except as may be expressly permitted in writing by the publisher.

ISBN : 978-81-87108-32-0

Printed in India

10 9 8

Contents

Ganesha's Divine Birth

Once, Goddess Parvati, wife of Lord Shiva, was getting ready for her bath. "Do not allow anyone to enter while I am in my private chamber," she ordered Nandi and asked him to stand guard at the entrance.

A few minutes later, Nandi saw Shiva approaching. *The goddess has asked me to stop anyone from entering. But Shiva is her husband. How can I stop him?* he wondered.

Meanwhile, Shiva entered Parvati's private chamber. The handmaids, who were applying turmeric to her, fled on seeing Shiva. Parvati too was surprised to see him inside despite her instructions. "How could Nandi let you in?" she asked.

"Parvati, have you forgotten that I am your husband?" replied Shiva laughingly. But Parvati was far from amused. *This has to stop! No gana (follower of Shiva) will ever be completely mine. I must have my own follower who will listen only to me,* she thought.

She then collected all the turmeric paste which had been applied on her body and created a form using it, and then breathed life into it. Lo and behold! A young boy stood in front of her.

"My son!" said Parvati and hugged the boy. "You are my son! You will listen only to your mother."

"Your wish is my command, mother," said the young boy.

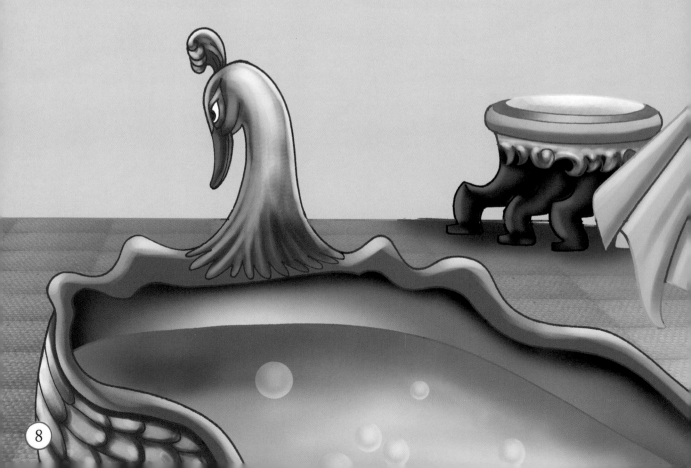

"Then go and guard the entrance. Do not allow anyone to enter," said Parvati and gave him a stick as a weapon.

The boy took his position outside her chamber. Soon, Shiva returned to meet Parvati. "Stop! Who goes there?" asked the boy.

"Son, you seem to be new here. I am Shiva, Parvati's husband," Shiva said.

"And, I am her son," said the boy. "My mother has ordered me not to let anyone through the door."

"But you don't seem to understand, I am her husband," Shiva said.

"I cannot allow anyone to go in," the boy repeated and raised his stick. Shiva pondered for a few minutes and left the place.

He called his ganas and instructed them to teach the boy a lesson. When the boy saw the ganas approaching, he was in doubt. They were Shiva's followers and he was Parvati's son. *How could he fight them?* But Parvati, sensing her son's dilemma, sent word through her handmaid that he was not to let anyone enter without her permission.

The boy was now confident and fought the ganas bravely. Soon, he had defeated all of them. Shiva was surprised to see his followers defeated. He asked Lord Brahma for help. "Do not worry, I will make him understand who you are," said Brahma and went to the boy disguised as a sage.

But the boy would not listen, and raised his stick on Brahma too.

Parvati was furious with the way Shiva was trying to persuade her son to let him enter. So she called upon Durga and Kali, her other avatars, to go and help her son.

Kali swallowed all the deadly weapons thrown at the boy by Shiva's followers, who had returned to fight, while Durga fought the other devas (gods) who had come to Shiva's help.

When there could not defeat the boy, Shiva finally took to the battlefield. Lord Vishnu flew into the battle on his Garuda, and as he kept the boy busy in combat, Shiva hurled his trishul (trident) at the boy.

The boy's head was severed from the body and he fell lifeless to the ground.

"Goddess, they have killed your son!" cried out Parvati's handmaids. Parvati was very angry. She created hundreds of shaktis (forms of her) in anger. "Go and avenge the death of my son," she ordered.The shaktis created havoc on the battlefield; killed hundreds of ganas and devas.

Brahma, Vishnu and Indra rushed to Shiva. "Please, console Parvati," they begged him.

Shiva thought for a few minutes and asked his ganas to bring him the head of the first living being that they see sleeping with its head in the wrong direction.

And the ganas found an elephant sleeping with its head in the northern direction. They cut the elephant's head and brought it back to Shiva. He placed the head on the lifeless body and within seconds, the boy arose—as if from a deep sleep. And everyone was very happy to see him.

"You have to give my son the most important position," Parvati demanded from Shiva.

"From today, he will be known as Ganesha and will be worshipped before anyone else," Shiva said. That is why Ganesha is the first to be worshipped at all auspicious occasions.

The Playful Child

Little Ganesha was a very playful child. He would easily get attracted to small things. One day, Lord Vishnu had come to visit Lord Shiva. While the two were deep in conversation, Lord Ganesha saw Vishnu's lethal weapon—the chakra—lying near him. He picked it up and started playing and rotating it, like a pinwheel.

Vishnu was so engrossed in his conversation that he did not pay attention to Ganesha's antics. *I love this chakra. Why don't I eat it?* thought Ganesha, and popped it into his mouth.

Soon, it was time for Lord Vishnu to leave. He looked for his chakra, but it was nowhere to be found! "Where could it be?" wondered Vishnu, and then realised, with his divine sight, that Ganesha had swallowed it.

How do I take it out from his stomach without hurting him? he thought.

If I ask him to give it back, he might not return it. However, if I have to get it back by force, he is very powerful, and it might turn into an ugly battle.

Then an idea struck him! He decided to make Ganesha laugh. The plan was to make him laugh so much, and so hard, that the chakra would come out of his stomach on its own (Ganesha was known for his hearty laugh—where his entire body would shake).

Vishnu made his way to Ganesha's chamber. "Look at me, Ganesha," he said. Then he caught hold of his ears with both his hands and acted as though he was sitting down,

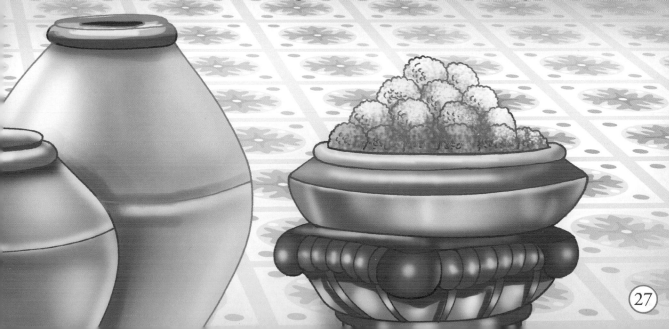

with his knees bent. But before Ganesha could realise what he was doing, he got up again. Vishnu went on performing such strange antics, till Ganesha started laughing heartily. Slowly and slowly, Vishnu had made him laugh so much that he spat out the chakra while laughing.

Vishnu was relieved, while Ganesha was more than happy with what he had seen.From then on, all the people visiting Ganesha's temples perform these actions in front of the Lord, to seek his forgiveness and blessings.

Ganesha Gets His Vehicle

Gajasura was a fierce elephant-headed demon, who performed severe penance for Lord Shiva's boon. At last, Shiva was pleased and appeared before him. "Gajasura, I am pleased with your dedication and want to grant you a boon," said Shiva.

"Dear Lord, let it be that I can be killed only by someone as dark as me in colour," asked Gajasura. Shiva granted him the boon and Gajasura created panic and havoc in all the three worlds.

All the gods ran to Shiva for help. In turn, he asked them to seek Lord Ganesha's help. And Ganesha challenged Gajasura to a fight. "You are too young to fight someone as powerful as me," said Gajasura arrogantly. But Ganesha fought him with such might, that Gajasura knew that his end was near.

He disguised himself as a rat and tried to run away. But Ganesha caught him and just when he was about to kill him Gajasura pleaded with him for mercy, "My Lord! Please, let me live and I will serve you all my life." Ganesha took pity on him and made him his vehicle. And, that is how the elephant-headed God got a tiny rat as his vehicle.

Ganesha Competes with His Brother

After Lord Ganesha, Lord Shiva and Goddess Parvati had another divine child called Kartikeya. One day, while Ganesha and Kartikeya were playing near their parents on Mount Kailash, sage Narada came to them with a divine mango.

"Lord Shiva, I seek your blessings. I bring you a divine mango, which can be given to one of your sons, as it cannot be cut. It has to be enjoyed as a whole," said Narada. Parvati and Shiva were in a dilemma. Which of their two sons could they give it to? Both of them were worthy of it and were equally loved. So, they decided to have a small race between their sons.

"The one who manages to circle around the whole world three times and comes back first, will win the divine mango," they declared.

Kartikeya did not waste even a minute. He mounted his vehicle—the peacock—and flew off. But Ganesha looked at his vehicle—the rat—and thought hard. How would he circle the world on such a slow vehicle? And then it struck him!

He happily started circling around his parents. Everyone was surprised. "Aren't you competing, my son?" asked Parvati.

"You and my father are the world for me, mother!" said Ganesha. "So, I am circling you thrice," he said and continued. When he had finished, Shiva gave him the mango.

Such was Ganesha's wisdom, which is why he is always worshipped by everyone seeking knowledge and wisdom.

Ganesha Curses the Moon

Lord Ganesha was known to be very fond of sweets. He was invited for a feast, where he ate with great delight. "Give me more," Ganesha said, enjoying the rich, delicious food.

Soon, it was time for everyone to leave. But poor Ganesha had overeaten and could barely walk. Lifting his big pot belly, he slowly walked back home. It was indeed a funny sight to see Ganesha struggling to with his full stomach. Chandra, the Moon God, could not contain himself, and started laughing at Ganesha. Ganesha felt insulted to see Chandra poking fun at him.

"Anyone who sees you on the day of Ganesh Chaturthi will be wrongly blamed and punished," Ganesha cursed angrily.

Chandra was petrified to see Ganesha so angry. He immediately begged him for forgiveness and asked him to take back his curse.

"A curse once given cannot be taken back. However, even if someone sees you on Ganesh Chaturthi, the curse will not take effect if they see you the next night as well," Ganesha said. Chandra thanked Ganesha for his kindness and benevolence.

Ganesha and Analasura

Analasura was a fire-breathing demon, who was causing havoc in the three worlds. All the gods ran to Lord Ganesha for help. "It is impossible to go near him. He breathes out fire at anyone who even dares to go near him," said Indra. "Only you can kill this demon and rid us of the terror he is causing," the other gods added.

Ganesha promised his protection to the gods and set out to fight Analasura. Ganesha knew that no weapon could subdue Analasura. So, he did something that no one could have thought of. He gripped Analasura with his trunk and swallowed him alive. But once Analasura was inside his stomach, Ganesha started feeling the heat.

"My stomach is on fire!" he cried out aloud.

The gods brought the water from the holy rivers and poured it on him, but his stomach continued to burn.

Then the gods put ice on his head to cool him down, but even that did not help. "Stop this burning!" cried Ganesha.

But the gods could not think of any other solution. They had even brought the moon and placed him on Ganesha's head to cool him down, but it did not give Ganesha any respite.

Finally, one of the sages brought the Durva (holy grass) and placed it on his head. Instantly, the burning in Ganesha's stomach stopped. He was so pleased that he said, "From this day, anyone who wants my blessing, should worship me with the holy grass."

Ganesha Humbles Kubera

Kubera, the God of Wealth, was very arrogant about his riches. One day, he decided to invite Lord Shiva's family to his city, Alakapuri, for a grand lunch. Shiva gave his consent and Kubera was overjoyed at this divine acceptance.

"Decorate Alakapuri like never before!" he ordered. Finally, it was time for the guests to arrive.

But Kubera was disappointed to see only Little Ganesha walking in for the feast. *How much can a child eat?* he thought and ordered a few dishes to be placed before him.

But Lord Ganesha ate the dishes within minutes and asked for more. Kubera ordered for more food. And Ganesha finished those dishes as well. "I want more," thundered Ganesha. Kubera kept feeding him and Ganesha kept asking for more. Soon, Kubera ran out of food in his palace and had to ask for more food to be brought from other houses.

He realised that something extraordinary was happening. He kneeled in front of Ganesha and said, "Lord! I have learnt my lesson. You have taught me that my riches are no match for even a child."

"Kubera, I wanted to teach you that even a fruit offered to me with humility means more to me than the food offered with arrogance," said Ganesha. This is how Kubera learnt the importance of humility.

Ganesha Shatters Ravana's Dreams

Ravana, the ruler of Lanka, was an ardent devotee of Lord Shiva. He would offer prayers to Shiva thrice a day. One day, after offering his prayers, a thought struck Ravana. "If I can get hold of an atmalinga (a reflection of Shiva), I can never be defeated by anyone," he thought.

So, he started performing the most severe of penances to please Shiva. The strongest of winds or the hottest of climates, could not break his focus. Shiva was impressed with Ravana's devotion and appeared before him.

"Ravana, you have pleased me with your devotion. Please ask for a boon and it will be granted," he said.

"Lord, I would be honoured to have an atmalinga of yours," replied Ravana.

"So be it," said Shiva and gave him a sparkling linga in his hand.

"But remember Ravana," Shiva warned, "if the linga is placed on the ground, it will establish itself there. After that, no one will be able to move it from that place."

"I will not put it down till I reach Lanka," said Ravana, and left for his capital city.

Meanwhile, the gods were worried. "Lord! Did you hear that Ravana now has the atmalinga?" one of the gods asked Lord Indra, the ruler of heaven.

"I know, and I am very worried," he replied. "If the linga reaches Lanka, no one can ever defeat Ravana. We must stop it from reaching Lanka."

But the gods were not sure who could help them. Then it struck them; Lord Ganesha was the all-powerful one who could help avert this from happening. So, they all went to Ganesha.

"Ganesha, Ravana has got the atmalinga from your father, and is on his way to Lanka. You are well aware of the destruction that

will happen if he becomes powerful. You are the only one who can save us," said Indra.

"And, Ravana had forgotten to offer his prayers to you before beginning his penance, like everyone else in the world does before starting anything auspicious," he added, fuelling Ganesha's anger.

"I assure you that the linga will not reach Lanka," assured Ganesha.

He then disguised himself as a shepherd and found Ravana walking with the linga in his hands. Ravana was in a dilemma. It was time for his daily prayers to Shiva. Yet, he could not put the linga down. So he looked around for help and found Ganesha disguised as the shepherd walking towards him.

"Young man! Will you hold this for me, while I offer my prayers and come back?" asked Ravana.

"I cannot! I am on my way home," replied the shepherd.

"I cannot break my ritual. Please hold this only for for a short while," pleaded Ravana.

"I will, on one condition," replied Ganesha. "I will call out to you three times, if I find it to be heavy. And if you don't come, when I call you, I will put it down," he said.

"I promise you that I will be back the first time you call me," said Ravana, and gave him the linga. He then walked towards the sea to offer his prayers. When Ganesha saw him beginning his prayers, he called out to him the first time, "Ravana, come back! It is too heavy for me!" Ravana had just begun his prayers, and thought to himself that he would run back after he called out the second time, as he had said earlier.

The second time came sooner than Ravana had imagined. Ganesha called out to him again. Ravana decided to finish his prayers immediately and run back. But by that time, Ganesha had given his third and final call. "I cannot bear the weight anymore, I am going to put it down!" he shouted out.

"No! Do not do that!" shouted Ravana, running back as fast as he could. "Please, don't let it touch the ground," he pleaded with the boy.

But it was too late! Ganesha had already placed the linga on the ground, just when Ravana was an arm's length away from him.

"How could you do this?" Ravana said angrily. "I kept my word. I called out to you three times. You did not return in time. Don't blame me Ravana," Ganesha said and walked away.

Upset, Ravana tried his best to uproot the linga. But the linga just grew bigger and bigger, with every attempt.

Soon, Ravana realised that nothing could be done to reverse what had happened. So, he sat there and offered his prayers to Lord Shiva.

The place where Ganesha put down the linga is called Gokarna. It is in Western India, and millions of pilgrims throng to this temple for a glimpse of the atmalinga.

Ganesha and His Broken Tusk

Sage Veda Vyasa was deep in meditation, when he suddenly thought of writing an epic. "Lord Brahma, only you can help me fulfil my desire," said Vyasa to Lord Brahma.

"I want to write an epic, but it needs to be written at an unimaginable speed as I recite it," he said. Lord Brahma thought for a while and said, "I can think of only Lord Ganesha."

Vyasa went to Ganesha with his request. And Ganesha put forth only one condition before taking on the task.

"You must not allow my pen to stop even once. This means that you have to recite without any pause," Ganesha said.

"I will recite continuously but you must not write any verse that you do not understand," said Vyasa.

Ganesha agreed and the two sat down to write the world's biggest epic—the Mahabharata. Ganesha needed a pen for this divine task. He could not find any, so he broke a part of one of his tusks to use as his pen.

Sage Vyasa recited without a break, and Ganesha understood every verse and wrote it at the speed of lightning.

OTHER TITLES IN THIS SERIES

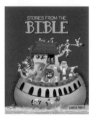

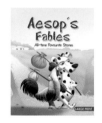
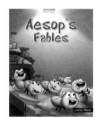

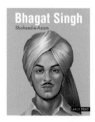
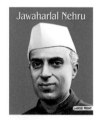
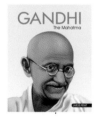

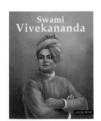

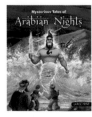

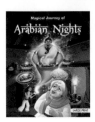